AFRICAN ART

Permanent Collection
Illinois State University
Normal-Bloomington

The Ewing Museum of Nations
Illinois State University Foundation

Ewing Museum of Nations

F. Louis Hoover
Editor

Photography:

Illinois State University
Photographic Services

Library of Congress Catalog Card Number: 74-28644

Preface

After nearly 30 years of service, it is appropriate that F. Louis Hoover's last official contribution to Illinois State University was the development of a fine collection of traditional African art.

Over the years, Dr. Hoover developed his avocation of collecting art while pursuing his vocation as an art educator. One of his major teaching and collecting interests has been the so-called "primitive" arts, but he had confined his private acquisitions primarily to the Americas.

The opportunity to combine his avocation and vocation came when he was asked to direct the University Museums and Galleries shortly after he had retired as chairman of the Art Department. Immediately Mr. and Mrs. Hoover donated portions of their personal collections to the University, and he began gathering support for African acquisitions. Cooperation of the University, the University Foundation, officials of governments and national museum directors made this project possible; but one man engendered our cooperation, and he has made us proud. His success is proved by this catalog.

We also take pride in the fact that a man of Dr. Frank Willett's reputation in the field of African anthropology and art history was interested in preparing the Introduction to this catalog. His book, *African Art*, and his writings in the *Encyclopedia Britanica* have served internationally to introduce millions to Africa and its art. We hope that this catalog will introduce our collection and its contribution to the study of African art, and we thank Professor Willett for his part in its publication.

It is not often that a museum embarks on a totally new area of acquisition; but when it is done, it is done with the full intent to maintain a vital collection. The University Museums will actively seek to improve our collection of African art and provide for public accessibility.

Arne Hansen
Director of Museums

Introduction

This book draws attention for the first time to an important collection of African sculpture, the great bulk of which was purchased in Africa by Dr. F. Louis Hoover during two visits in the Springs of 1972 and 1973. That he was able to obtain so much, of such a high standard in such a short time speaks as highly of his industry as it does of his judgement. The Administration of Illinois State University is to be congratulated on its decision to invite Dr. Hoover to make these trips, for it would probably be impossible to assemble such a collection today in this way. Any university which wished to build up a comparable collection nowadays would find the cost prohibitive. Moreover, these pieces were all collected and exported with the agreement of the appropriate local authority, thus demonstrating that good pieces can be obtained legitimately without recourse to smuggling.

It is an especial joy to me that this material was collected, not for Dr. Hoover's personal gain or even professional advancement (for he was about to retire when he made these trips), but purely so that it should be available not only to the University but also to the entire community for study and enjoyment.

Very few collections are evenly balanced: it would be very dull if all collections were similar. Since this material was mainly collected in West Africa the sculpture of the Congo Basin is barely represented, nor are there many Yoruba pieces. Nevertheless, the number of pieces from Upper Volta (with attributions made by Dr. Triande, Director of the National Museum in Ouagadougou) form probably the best collection anywhere in America.

Similarly the helmet masks for the Sande (women's initiation) society in Liberia and Sierra Leone are a very important group which demonstrates well the great amount of freedom of expression permitted to the artist even when he was required to adhere to a closely restricted formula. Again there are a large number of masks of the Dan-Ngere complex of Liberia and Ivory Coast, an interesting group of peoples who have been studied in the field by several scholars who have failed to reach agreement on their functions and meanings. There are also some good pieces of Dogon sculpture, varied and not repetitive examples of the work of the one group of people who have been studied more intensively than any other in Africa.

This collection then forms a remarkably good educational facility. African art is commonly taught from photographs and slides but these are inadequate substitutes for the original sculptures. Illinois State University now has one of the best collections of African sculpture in the State of Illinois. It is one which is especially suited for teaching, for its major clusters of objects will encourage investigation by graduate students in seminars, whilst the overall cover gives excellent support to general teaching of African art. It is to be hoped that the University community will make increasing use of this excellent and unusual facility, which will certainly attract scholars from elsewhere to visit the Ewing Museum of Nations.

Frank Willett
Northwestern University
September 1974

Contents

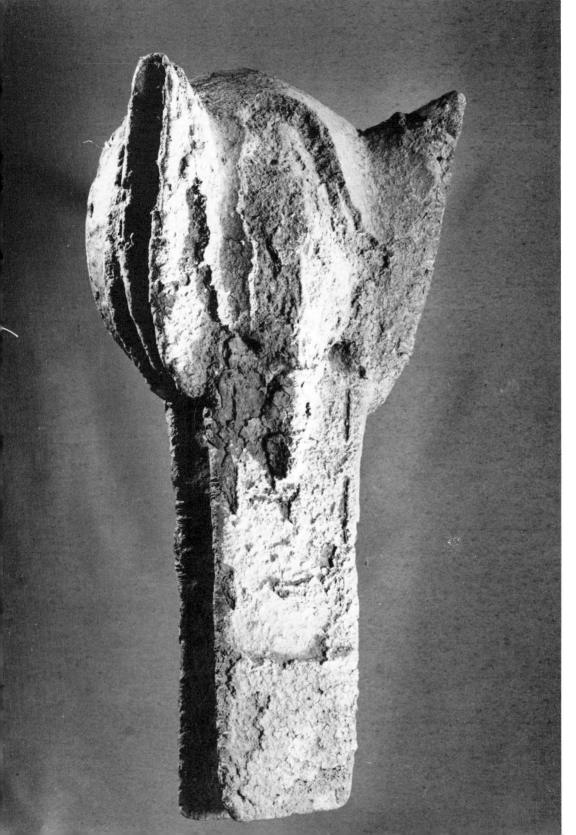

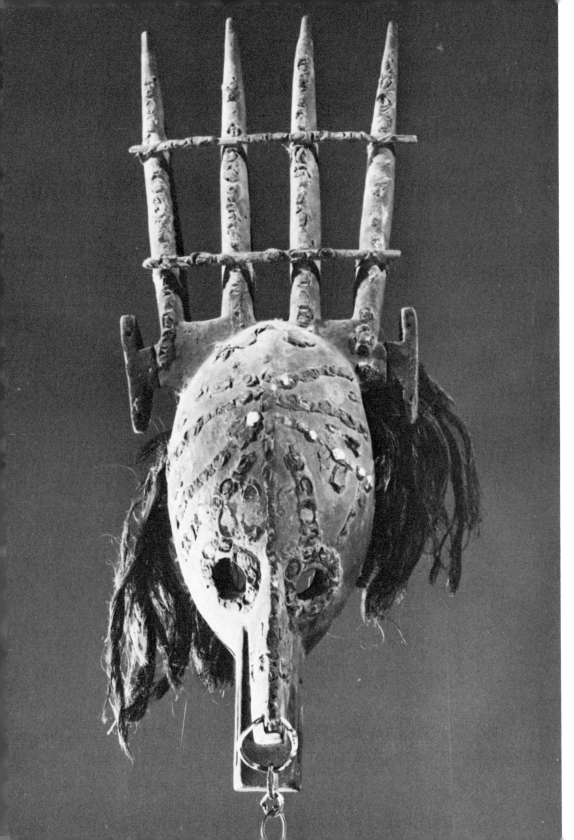

5

THE WESTERN SUDAN

1. Fetish Figure
   BAMBARA people, Mali
   Wood with encrustation
   22'' (55.9 cm.) long
   Acq. No. 7239

2. Mask
   BAMBARA people, Mali
   Wood with encrustation
   32'' (81.3 cm.) high
   Acq. No. 7333

3. Mask
   BAMBARA people, Mali
   Wood with shells
   18 5/8'' (47.3 cm.) high
   Acq. No. 7094

4. Mask
   BAMBARA people, Mali
   Wood with horns and fabric
   18 1/4'' (46.3 cm.) high
   Acq. No. 7309

5. Mask
   BAMBARA people, Mali
   Wood with shells and encrustation
   27'' (68.5 cm.) high
   Acq. No. 7334

6. Seated Female Figure
   BAMBARA people, Mali
   Wood, 30'' (76.2 cm.) high
   Acq. No. 7191

7. Antelope Headpiece
   BAMBARA people, Mali
   Wood, 48 1/4'' (122.5 cm.) high
   Acq. No. 7294

8. Antelope Headpiece
   BAMBARA people, Mali
   Wood, 65'' (165 cm.) high
   Acq. No. 7295

9. Antelope Headpiece
   BAMBARA people, Mali
   Wood, 52 1/4'' (132.7 cm.) high
   Acq. No. 7477

13

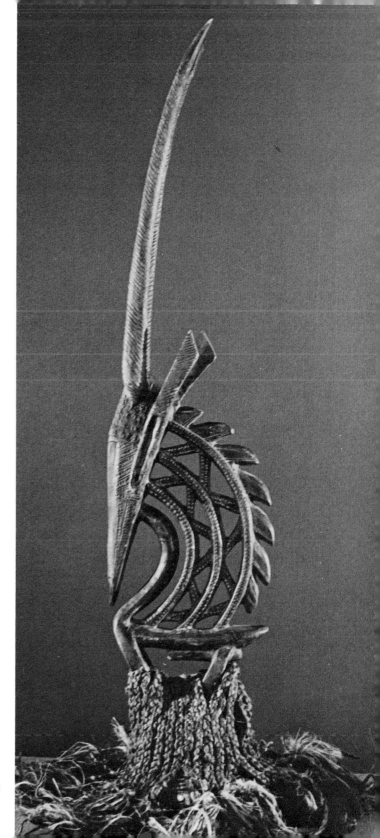

THE WESTERN SUDAN

10. Antelope Headpiece
    BAMBARA people, Mali
    Wood with shells, fiber, and mirrors
    20" (50.8 cm.) high
    Acq. No. 7085

11. Antelope Headpiece
    BAMBARA people, Mali
    Wood, 27" (68.5 cm.) high
    Acq. No. 7331

12. Antelope Headpiece
    BAMBARA people, Mali
    Wood, 22 9/16" (57.3 cm.) high
    Acq. No. 7185

13. Antelope Headpiece
    BAMBARA people, Mali
    Wood with fiber, 42" (106.6 cm.) high
    Acq. No. 7093

14

14. Stool
    BAMBARA people, Mali
    Wood, 13 5/8" (34.6 cm.) high
    Acq. No. 7298

15. Geneological Figure
    BAMBARA people, Mali
    Wood with metal, 68" (172.7 cm.) high
    Acq. No. 7292

16. Geneological Figure
    BAMBARA people, Mali
    Wood with metal and pigment
    53" (134.6 cm.) high
    Acq. No. 7302

17. Standing Female Figure
    BAMBARA people, Mali
    Wood, 50 3/16" (127.4 cm.) high
    Acq. No. 7305

18. Seated Male Figure
    BAMBARA people, Mali
    Wood, 22 5/8" (57.5 cm.) high
    Acq. No. 7324

19. Mask
    BAMBARA people, Mali
    Wood, 24 7/8" (63.2 cm.) high
    Acq. No. 7303

20. Cow Mask
    BAMBARA people, Mali
    Wood with pigment
    23 11/16" (60.2 cm.) high
    Acq. No. 7332

21. Game Board
    BAMBARA people, Mali
    Wood, 33 3/4" (85.7 cm.) long
    Acq. No. 7321

22. Bracelet
    BAMBARA people, Mali
    Brass, 2 3/4" (7 cm.) diameter
    Acq. No. 7224

20

23. Bracelet
    BAMBARA people, Mali
    Brass, 2 7/8'' (7.3 cm.) diameter
    Acq. No. 7223

24. Bracelet
    BAMBARA people, Mali
    Bronze, 3 3/16'' (8.1 cm.) diameter
    Acq. No. 7222

25. Mask
    BOBO people, Upper Volta
    Wood, 18 3/4'' (47.6 cm.) high
    Acq. No. 7116

26. Helmet Mask
    BOBO people, Upper Volta
    Wood with pigment
    57 7/8'' (147 cm.) long
    Acq. No. 7463

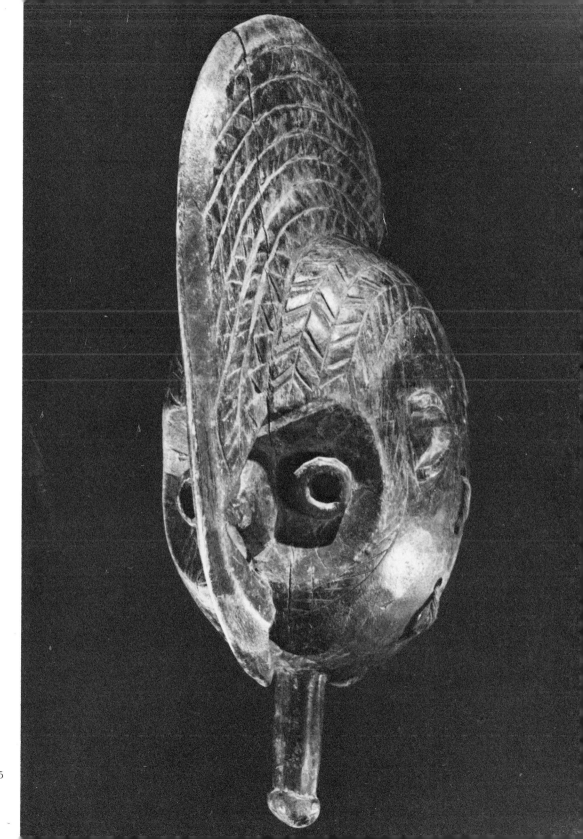

25

THE WESTERN SUDAN

27. Mask
    BOBO people, Upper Volta
    Wood, 36 5/8'' (93 cm.) high
    Acq. No. 7281

28. Mask
    BOBO people, Upper Volta
    Wood, 32'' (81.3 cm.) high
    Acq. No. 7238

29. Snake Mask
    BOBO people, Upper Volta
    Wood with pigment
    98 15/16'' (251.1 cm.) long
    Acq. No. 7429

30. Crocodile Mask
    BOBO people, Upper Volta
    Wood with pigment
    84'' (213.4 cm.) long
    Acq. No. 7430

31. Mask
    BOBO people, Upper Volta
    Wood, 32 3/4'' (83.2 cm.) high) high
    Acq. No. 7296

32. Helmet Mask
    BOBO people, Upper Volta
    Wood with pigment
    66 5/16'' (168.4 cm.) high
    Acq. No. 7457

33. Headpiece
    BOBO people, Upper Volta
    Wood with pigment
    22'' (55.9 cm.) long
    Acq. No. 7225

34. Gourd Container
    BOBO people, Upper Volta
    Gourd, 13 1/4'' (33.6 cm.) high
    Acq. No. 7089

35. Set of Eleven Baskets
    BOBO people, Upper Volta
    Woven grass with hide
    Acq. No. 7100

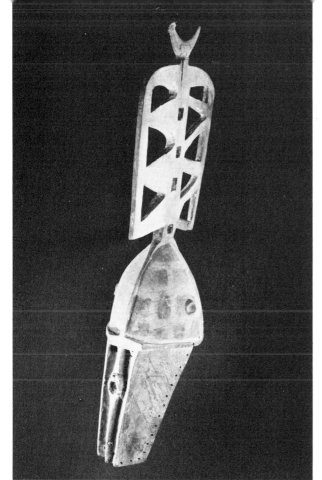

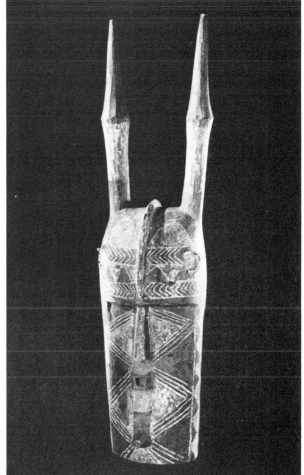

38

39

36. Bracelet
   BOBO people, Upper Volta
   Bronze, 3 7/8'' (9.9. cm.) diameter
   Acq. No. 7316

37. Bracelet
   BOBO people, Upper Volta
   Bronze, 4 1/8'' (10.5 cm.) diameter
   Acq. No. 7315

38. Mask
   BOBO-FING people, Upper Volta
   Wood, 39 1/4'' (99.7 cm.) high
   Acq. No. 7385

39. Mask
   BOBO-FING people, Upper Volta
   Wood with pigment
   40 3/4'' (103.5 cm.) high
   Acq. No. 7434

40. Flute
   BOBO-FING people, Upper Volta
   Wood, 17 15/16'' (54.4 cm.) long
   Acq. No. 7392

41. Mask
   BOBO-FING people, Upper Volta
   Wood with pigment
   40 1/4'' (102.2 cm.) high
   Acq. No. 7307

THE WESTERN SUDAN

42. Mask
BWA people, Upper Volta
Wood, 32 1/2" (82.5 cm.) high
Acq. No. 7359

43. Mask
BWA people, Upper Volta
Wood with pigment, 29 3/4" (75.5 cm.) h
Acq. No. 7360

44. Mask
BWA people, Upper Volta
Wood with pigment
27 3/8" (69.5 cm.) high
Acq. No. 7336

45. Mask
BWA people, Upper Volta
Wood with pigment
42 1/8" (107 cm.) high
Acq. No. 7358

46. Mask
BWA people, Upper Volta
Wood with pigment
20 1/4" (51.4 cm.) high
Acq. No. 6955

47. Mask
DOGON people, Mali
Wood, 26 7/8" (68.3 cm.) high
Acq. No. 7330

48. Mask
DOGON people, Mali
Wood, 29 1/2" (75 cm.) high
Acq. No. 7323

49. Mask
DOGON people, Mali
Wood, 37" (97 cm.) high
Acq. No. 7329

50. Mask
DOGON people, Mali
Wood, 18" (45.8 cm.) high
Acq. No. 7233

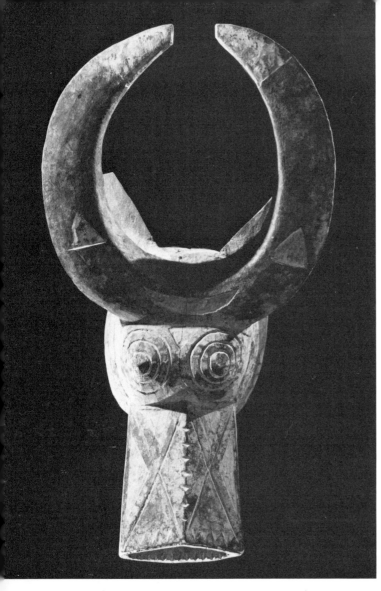

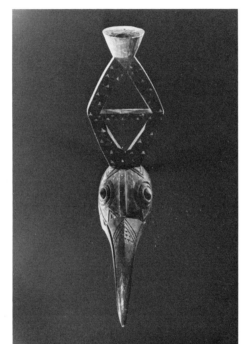

42   43   33

51. Mask
   DOGON people, Mali
   Wood, 20 1/4'' (51.5 cm.) high
   Acq. No. 7326

52. Mask
   DOGON people, Mali
   Wood, 14 1/8''(36 cm.) high
   Acq. No. 7325

53. Granary Door
   DOGON people, Mali
   Wood, 28 1/2'' (72.4 cm.) high
   Acq. No. 7310

47

48

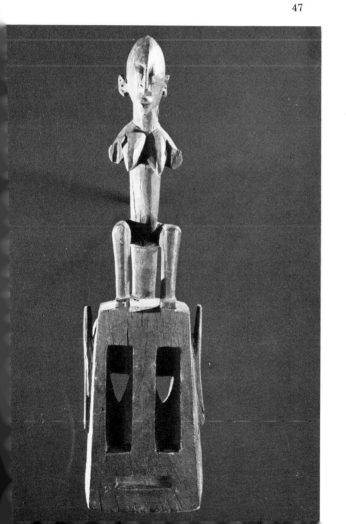

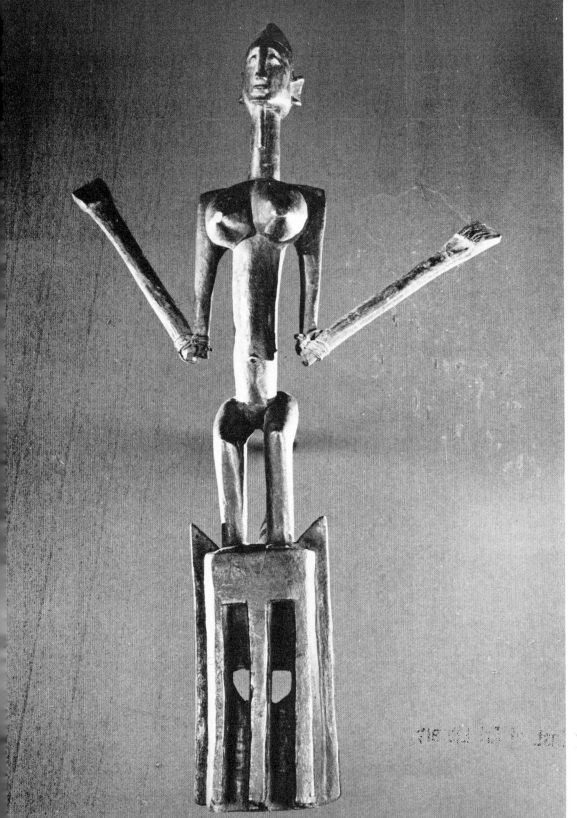

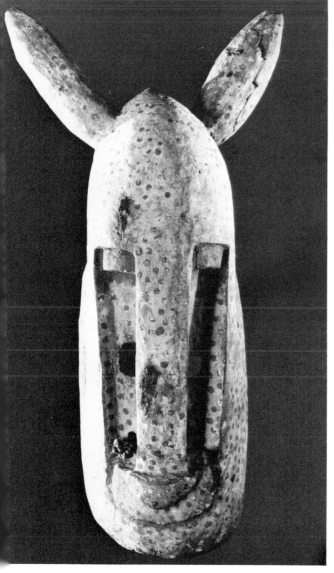

51

52

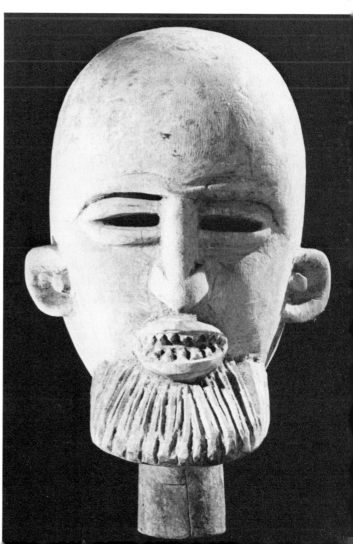

54. Standing Male Figure
    DOGON people, Mali
    Wood, 40 1/2'' (103 cm.) high
    Acq. No. 7284

55. Seated Mother and Child
    DOGON people, Mali
    Wood with pigment
    46 1/16'' (116.9 cm.) high
    Acq. No. 7283

56. Standing Female Figure
    DOGON people, Mali
    Wood, 29 5/8'' (74.5 cm.) high
    Acq. No. 7246

57. Mask
    DOGON people, Mali
    Wood, 32 5/8'' (82.9 cm.) high
    Acq. No. 7328

58. Vessel with Lid
    DOGON people, Mali
    Wood, 33 1/4'' (84.5 cm.) high
    Acq. No. 7327

59. Oil Lamp
    DOGON people, Mali
    Iron, 27 1/2'' (70 cm.) high
    Acq. No. 7297A

60. Oil Lamp
    DOGON people, Mali
    Iron, 27 1/2'' (70 cm.) high
    Acq. No. 7297B

61. Standing Male Figure
    DOGON people, Mali
    Wood, 13 9/16'' (34.2 cm.) high
    Acq. No. 7143

62. Standing Female Figure
    DOGON people, Mali
    Wood, 47 1/2'' (121.6 cm.) high
    Acq. No. 7084

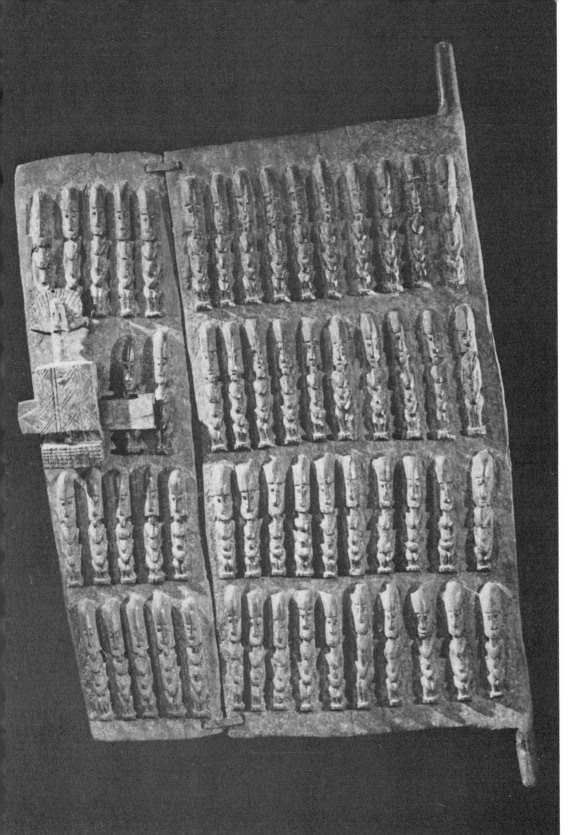

63. Crocodile
    DOGON people, Mali
    Wood, 43 3/4'' (111 cm.) long
    Acq. No. 7293

64. Hermaphroditic Figure
    DOGON people, Mali
    Wood, 22 3/4'' (57.8 cm.) high
    Acq. No. 7164

65. Kneeling Female Figure
    DOGON people, Mali
    Wood, 31 1/2'' (80 cm.) high
    Acq. No. 7190

66. Stool
    DOGON people, Mali
    Wood, 9 1/2'' (24 cm.) high
    Acq. No. 7124

67. Stool
    DOGON people, Mali
    Wood, 14 3/4'' (37.5 cm.) high
    Acq. No. 7300

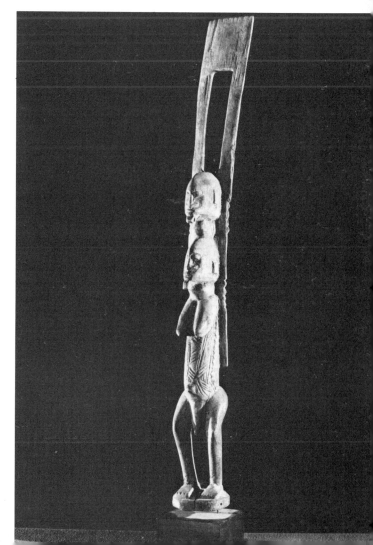

66

68. Stool
    DOGON people, Mali
    Wood, 14 3/4'' (37.5 cm.) high
    Acq. No. 7299

69. Dance Costume
    DOGON people, Mali
    Cloth and cowrie shells
    Acq. No. 7242

70. Standing Male Figure
    DOGON people, Mali
    Wood, 19 1/4'' (49 cm.) high
    Acq. No. 7140

71. Door Lock
    DOGON people, Mali
    Wood 13 5/8'' (34.6 cm.) high
    Acq. No. 7382

67

68

THE WESTERN SUDAN

72. Door Lock
    DOGON people, Mali
    Wood, 13 7/8'' (35.2 cm.) high
    Acq. No. 7381

73. Door Lock
    DOGON people, Mali
    Wood, 9 3/8'' (23.8 cm.) high
    Acq. No. 7400

74. Walking Stick
    DOGON people, Mali
    Wood, 37 1/2'' (94.6 cm.) long
    Acq. No. 7391

75. Vessel with Lid
    DOGON people, Mali
    Wood, 30 3/4'' (78 cm.) high
    Acq. No. 7306

76. Mask
    GURUNSI people, Upper Volta
    Wood with pigment
    38 3/4'' (98.5 cm.) high
    Acq. No. 7433

77. Mask
    GURUNSI people, Upper Volta
    Wood with pigment
    48'' (121.9 cm.) high
    Acq. No. 7373

78. Loom Heddle Pulley
    GURUNSI people, upper Volta
    Wood, 11'' (28 cm.) high
    Acq. No. 7393

79. Spoon
    GURUNSI people, Upper Volta
    Ivory, 7 5/8'' (19.4 cm.) long
    Acq. No. 7451

80. Anklet
    URUNSI people, Upper Volta
    Bronze, 7'' (17.7 cm.) long
    Acq. No. 7372

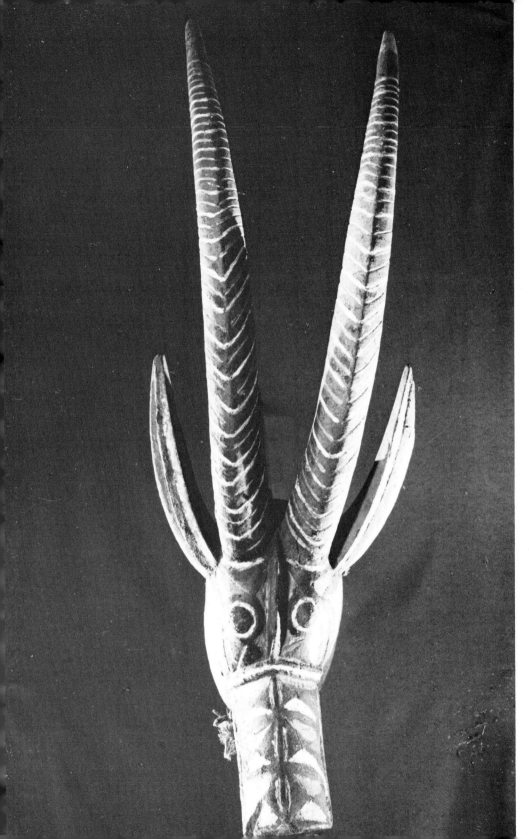

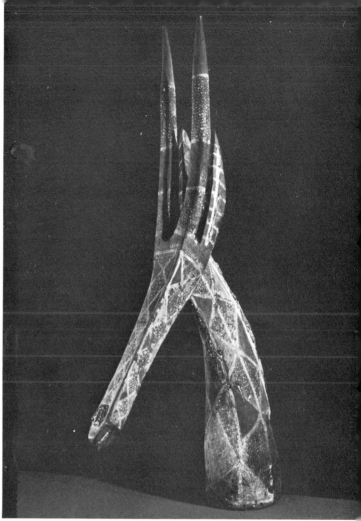

81. Bracelet
    GURUNSI people, Upper Volta
    Bronze, 5'' (12.7 cm.) diameter
    Acq. No. 7398

82. Bracelet
    GURUNSI people, Upper Volta
    Bronze, 5 1/2'' (14 cm.) diameter
    Acq. No. 7399

83. Bracelet
    GURUNSI people, Upper Volta
    Wood, 4 3/8'' (11.1 cm.) diameter
    Acq. No. 7396

87

88

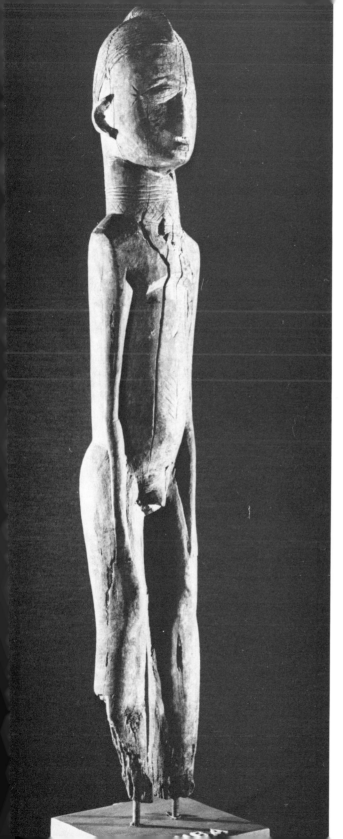

THE WESTERN SUDAN

84. Bracelet
    GURUNSI people, Upper Volta
    Ivory 4 5/8'' (11.8 cm.) diameter
    Acq. No. 7397

85. Antelope Mask
    KURUMBA people, Upper Volta
    Wood with pigment and seeds
    42 1/2'' (107.9 cm.) high
    Acq. No. 7460

86. Mask
    LOBI people, Upper Volta
    Wood with pigment
    10 3/4'' (27.3 cm.) high
    Acq. No. 6957

87. Standing Male Figure
    LOBI people, Upper Volta
    Wood, 14 1/4'' (36.2 cm.) high
    Acq. No. 7144

88. Standing Female Figure
    LOBI people, Upper Volta
    Wood, 11 7/8'' (30.2 cm.) high
    Acq. No. 7165

89. Standing Male Figure
    LOBI people, Upper Volta
    Wood, 34 5/8'' (88 cm.) high
    Acq. No. 7108

91/90/92

90. Standing Male Figure
    LOBI people, Upper Volta
    Wood, 32 7/8'' (83.5 cm.) high
    Acq. No. 7435

91. Standing Female Figure
    LOBI people, Upper Volta
    Wood, 16 5/8'' (42.2 cm.) high
    Acq. No. 6958

92. Standing Female Figure
    LOBI people, Upper Volta
    Wood, 16 7/16'' (41.6 cm.) high
    Acq. No. 7301

93. Mask
    MOSSI people, Upper Volta
    Wood with pigment, 13'' (33 cm.) long
    Acq. No. 7390

94. Mask
    MOSSI people, Upper Volta
    Wood, 27'' (68.6 cm.) high
    Acq. No. 7231

97

THE WESTERN SUDAN

95. Mask
MOSSI people, Upper Volta
Wood with pigment
12 1/2'' (31.7 cm.) long
Acq. No. 7450

96. Mask
MOSSI people, Upper Volta
Wood with pigment
57 1/8'' (145 cm.) high
Acq. No. 7291

97. Headpiece
MOSSI people, Upper Volta
Wood with shells and fiber
8 1/4'' (21 cm.) high
Acq. No. 7377

98. Mask
MOSSI people, Upper Volta
Wood with pigment and fiber
41'' (104 cm.) high
Acq. No. 7379

99. Mask and Costume
MOSSI people, Upper Volta
Wood with fiber
81 3/4'' (207.7 cm.) high
Acq. No. 7432

100. Mask
MOSSI people, Upper Volta
Wood with fiber and attached fetish
16 1/4'' (41.3 cm.) high
Acq. No. 7431

101. Standing Male Figure
MOSSI people, Upper Volta
Wood with pigment
20 7/16'' (51.9 cm.) high
Acq. No. 7388

102. Standing Female Figure
MOSSI people, Upper Volta
Wood with pigment
20 7/8'' (53 cm.) high
Acq. No. 7389

103. Standing Female Figure
MOSSI people, Upper Volta
Wood, 22 11/16'' (57.6 cm.) high
Acq. No. 7384

104. Seated Male Figure
MOSSI people, Upper Volta
Bronze, 9 11/16'' (24.6 cm.) high
Acq. No. 7313

105. Standing Female Figure
MOSSI people, Upper Volta
Wood with Cloth
25 1/16'' (63.7 cm.) high
Acq. No. 7374

106. Seated Mother and Child
MOSSI people, Upper Volta
Bronze, 9 3/8'' (23.8 cm.) high
Acq. No. 7314

107. Mask
MOSSI people, Upper Volta
Wood with encrustation
25 5/8'' (65.1 cm.) high
Acq. No. 7380

108. Headpiece
MOSSI people, Upper Volta
Wood with pigment, cloth, and fiber
11'' (28 cm.) high
Acq. No. 7378

109. Doll
MOSSI people, Upper Volta
Wood, 8 1/2'' (21.6 cm.) high
Acq. No. 7401

110. Doll
MOSSI people, Upper Volta
Wood, 8 1/4'' (21 cm.) high
Acq. No. 7402

111. Doll
MOSSI people, Upper Volta
Wood, 7 1/4'' (18.5 cm.) high
Acq. No. 7403

99

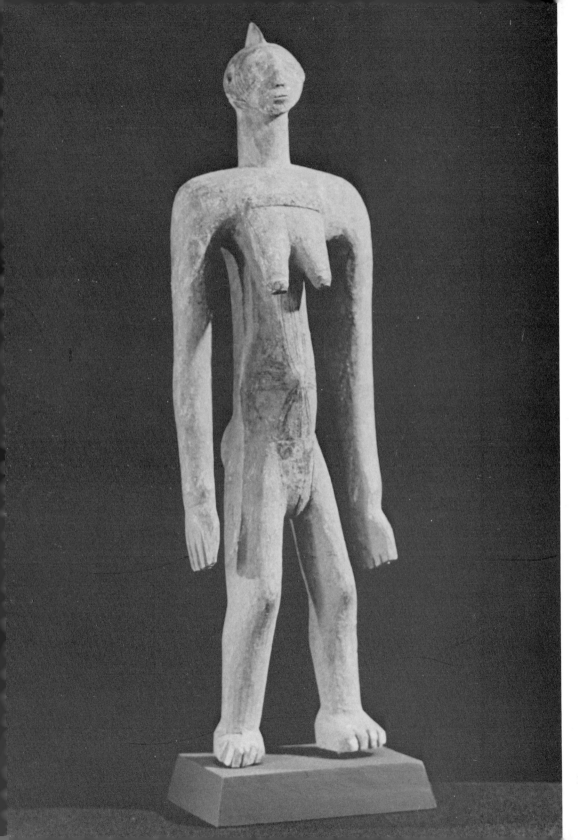

103

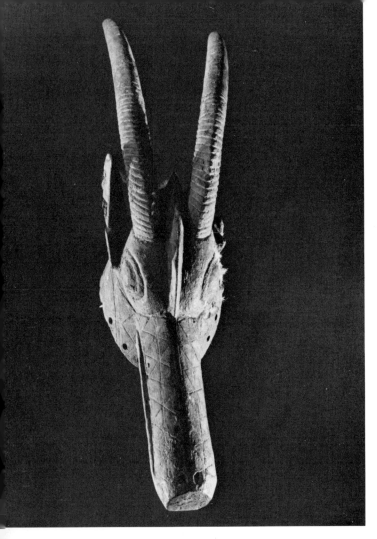

112. Doll
     MOSSI people, Upper Volta
     Wood, 11 1/2'' (29.2 cm.) high
     Acq. No. 7404

113. Doll
     MOSSI people, Upper Volta
     Wood, 9'' (22.9 cm.) high
     Acq. No. 7405

114. Doll
     MOSSI people, Upper Volta
     Wood, 8 1/2'' (21.6 cm.) high
     Acq. No. 7406

THE WESTERN SUDAN

115. Doll
   MOSSI people, Upper Volta
   Wood, 8 1/2" (21.6 cm.) high
   Acq. No. 7407

116. Doll
   MOSSI people, Upper Volta
   Wood, 11 1/4" (28.6 cm.) high
   Acq. No. 7408

117. Doll
   MOSSI people, Upper Volta
   Wood, 9 1/2" (24.2 cm.) high
   Acq. No. 7409

118. Doll
   MOSSI people, Upper Volta
   Wood, 8 1/4" (21 cm.) high
   Acq. No. 7410

119. Doll
   MOSSI people, Upper Volta
   Wood, 10" (25.4 cm.) high
   Acq. No. 7411

120. Doll
   MOSSI people, Upper Volta
   Wood, 9 1/2" (24.2 cm.) high
   Acq. No. 7412

121. Doll
   MOSSI people, Upper Volta
   Wood, 9" (22.9 cm.) high
   Acq. No. 7413

122. Doll
   MOSSI people, Upper Volta
   Wood, 6 3/4" (17.2 cm.) high
   Acq. No. 7414

123. Doll
   MOSSI people, Upper Volta
   Wood, 7" (17.8 cm.) high
   Acq. No. 7415

124. Doll
     MOSSI people, Upper Volta
     Wood, 8" (20.3 cm.) high
     Acq. No. 7416

125. Doll
     MOSSI people, Upper Volta
     Wood, 8" (20.3 cm.) high
     Acq. No. 7417

126. Doll
     MOSSI people, Upper Volta
     Wood, 6 1/4" (15.9 cm.) high
     Acq. No. 7418

127. Doll
     MOSSI people, Upper Volta
     Wood, 6 3/4" (17.2 cm.) high
     Acq. No. 7419

128. Doll
     MOSSI people, Upper Volta
     Wood, 8 3/4" (22.2 cm.) high
     Acq. No. 7420

129. Doll
     MOSSI people, Upper Volta
     Wood, 10 1/2" (26.8 cm.) high
     Acq. No. 7421

130. Doll
     MOSSI people, Upper Volta
     Wood, 7 1/4" (18.4 cm.) high
     Acq. No. 7422

131. Door Lock
     MOSSI people, Upper Volta
     Wood, 23 5/16" (59.2 cm.) high
     Acq. No. 7375

132. Door Lock
     MOSSI people, Upper Volta
     Wood, 22" (55.9 cm.) high
     Acq. No. 7376

133. Hair Ornaments (five)
     MOSSI people, Upper Volta
     Bronze, 3 1/8" (8 cm.) long
     Acq. No. 7371

134. Hair Ornament
     MOSSI people, Upper Volta
     Ivory, 4 7/8" (12.4 cm.) long
     Acq. No. 7370

135. Bracelet
     MOSSI people, Upper Volta
     Bronze, 2 15/16" (7.5 cm.) diameter
     Acq. No. 7365

136. Bracelet
     MOSSI people, Upper Volta
     Bronze, 3" (7.6 cm.) diameter
     Acq. No. 7366

THE WESTERN SUDAN

137. Bracelet
MOSSI people, Upper Volta
Bronze, 3 3/4'' (9.5 cm.) diameter
Acq. No. 7364

138. Bracelet
MOSSI people, Upper Volta
Bronze, 3 7/8'' (10 cm.) diameter
Acq. No. 7367

139. Bracelet
MOSSI people, Upper Volta
Bronze, 4'' (10.1 cm.) diameter
Acq. No. 7363

140. Bracelets (pair)
MOSSI people, Upper Volta
Stone, 3 7/8'' (9.9 cm.) diameter
Acq. No. 7395

141. Belt
MOSSI people, Upper Volta
Shell, 32'' (81.2 cm.) long
Acq. No. 7361

142. Belt
MOSSI people, Upper Volta
Shell and glass beads
32'' (81.2 cm.) long
Acq. No. 7362

109-130

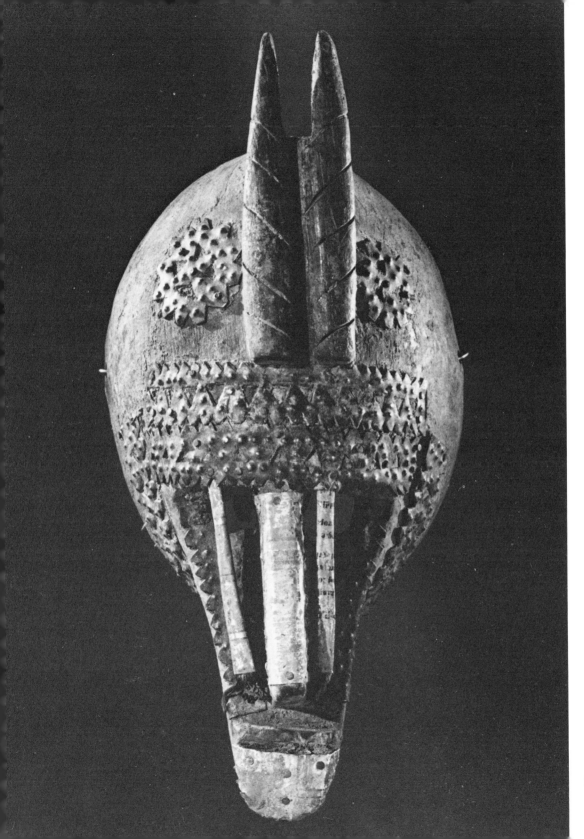

145

143. Door Lock
SAMO people, Upper Volta
Wood, 24 1/4'' (61.5 cm.) high
Acq. No. 7383

144. Dance Costume
SAMO people, Upper Volta
Shells, Cloth, and hide
Acq. No. 7452

145. Mask
SARAKOLE people, Mali
Wood with metal and pigment
13'' (33 cm.) high
Acq. No. 7320

146. Standing Male Figure
SENUFO people, Ivory Coast
Wood, 55 15/16'' (141.8 cm.) high
Acq. No. 7352

147. Vessel with Lid
SENUFO people, Ivory Coast
Wood, 31 1/2'' (80 cm.) high
Acq. No. 7340

148. Mask
SENUFO people, Ivory Coast
Wood with pigment
32 1/2'' (82.6 cm.) long
Acq. No. 7121

149. Male Rhythm Pounder
SENUFO people, Ivory Coast
Wood, 36 1/2'' (92.7 cm.) high
Acq. No. 7091

150. Mask
SENUFO people, Ivory Coast
Wood with pigment
28 1/2'' (72.4 cm.) long
Acq. No. 7167

151. Bird
SENUFO people, Ivory Coast
Wood, 79 3/4'' (202.5 cm.) high
Acq. No. 7436

152. Seated Female Figure
SENUFO people, Ivory Coast
Wood, 12 7/8'' (32.8 cm.) high
Acq. No. 7141

153. Mask
SENUFO people, Ivory Coast
Wood, 29 1/8'' (74 cm.) high
Acq. No. 7308

154. Standing Female Figure
SENUFO people, Ivory Coast
Wood, 8 1/2'' (21.6 cm.) high
Acq. No. 7137

155. Standing Female Figure
SENUFO people, Ivory Coast
Wood, 8 1/4'' (21 cm.) high
Acq. No. 7138

156. Mask
SENUFO people, Ivory Coast
Wood with feathers and hide
17 1/16'' (43.3 cm.) high
Acq. No. 7118

157. Seated Figure
SENUFO people, Ivory Coast
Wood, 34 3/4'' (88.2 cm.) high
Acq. No. 7425

158. Bird
SENUFO people, Ivory Coast
Wood, 59 1/2'' (151 cm.) high
Acq. No. 7237

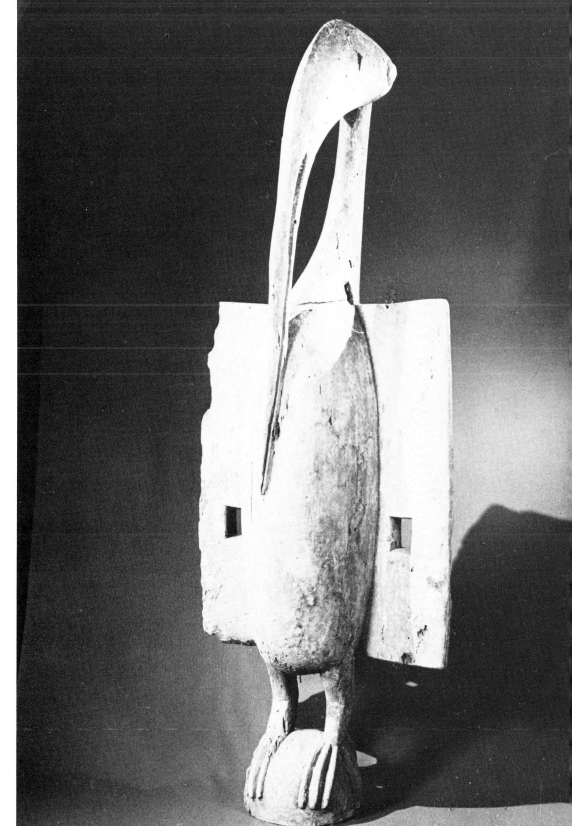

159. Seated Female Figure
SENUFO people, Ivory Coast
Wood, 12 7/16" (31.6 cm.) high
Acq. No. 7145

160. Ceremonial Harvest Birds
SENUFO people, Ivory Coast
Wood with feathers and fibers
16 1/4" (41.3 cm.) long
Acq. No. 7087

161. Ceremonial Staff
SENUFO people, Ivory Coast
Wood, 12 1/2" (31.7 cm.) figure height
Acq. No. 7128

162. Standing Female Figure
SENUFO people, Ivory Coast
Wood, 15 5/8" (39.7 cm.) high
Acq. No. 7286

163. Ceremonial Staff Ornament
SENUFO people, Ivory Coast
Wood, 13 5/8" (34.6 cm.) high
Acq. No. 7126

164. Ceremonial Staff Ornament
SENUFO people, Ivory Coast
Wood, 11" (28 cm.) high
Acq. No. 7127

165. Buffalo
SENUFO people (?), Ivory Coast
Bronze, 12 11/16" (32.3 cm.) long
Acq. No. 7339

166. Ceremonial Staff Ornament
SENUFO people, Ivory Coast
Wood, 8 1/2" (21 cm.) high
Acq. No. 7125

167. Ceremonial Sword
SENUFO people, Ivory Coast
Wood, 38 3/4" (98.5 cm.) long
Acq. No. 7241

168. Warrior's Shirt
SENUFO people, Ivory Coast
Cloth with amulets
27" x 33" (68.6 x 83.8 cm.)
Acq. No. 7465

169. Warrior's Helmet
SENUFO people, Ivory Coast
Hide, horns, shells, and cloth
13 1/2" (34.3 cm.) high
Acq. No. 7466

170. Bracelet
SENUFO people, Ivory Coast
Brass, 2 7/8" (7.3 cm.) diameter
Acq. No. 7210

171. Bracelet
SENUFO people, Ivory Coast
Brass, 2 3/4" (7 cm.) diameter
Acq. No. 7211

172. Bracelet
SENUFO people, Ivory Coast
Brass, 2 7/8" (7.3 cm.) diameter
Acq. No. 7209

173. Bracelet
SENUFO people, Ivory Coast
Brass, 2 1/2" (6.4 cm.) diameter
Acq. No. 7213

174. Bracelet
SENUFO people, Ivory Coast
Brass, 2 3/4" (7 cm.) diameter
Acq. No. 7214

175. Bracelet
SENUFO people, Ivory Coast
Brass, 2 1/16" (5.2 cm.) diameter
Acq. No. 7212

176. Bracelet
SENUFO people, Ivory Coast
Brass, 2 3/4" (7 cm.) diameter
Acq. No. 7216

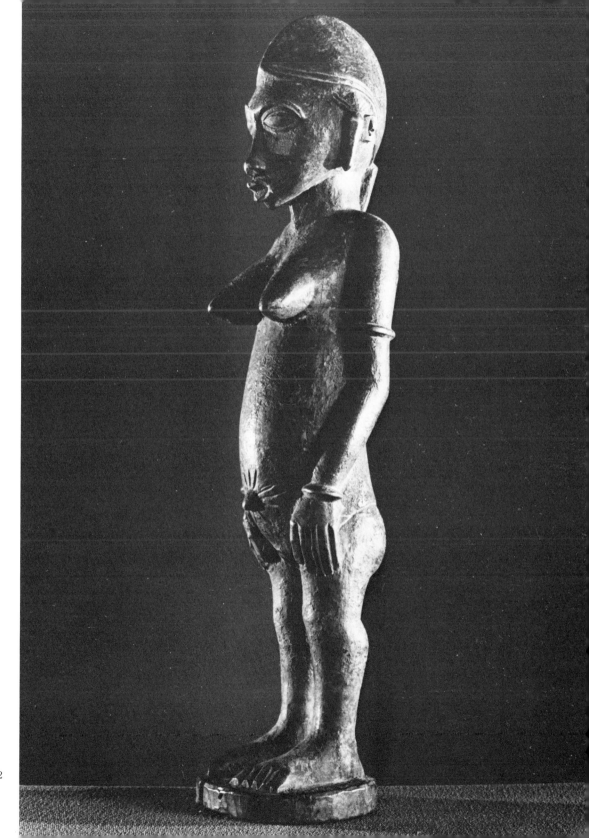

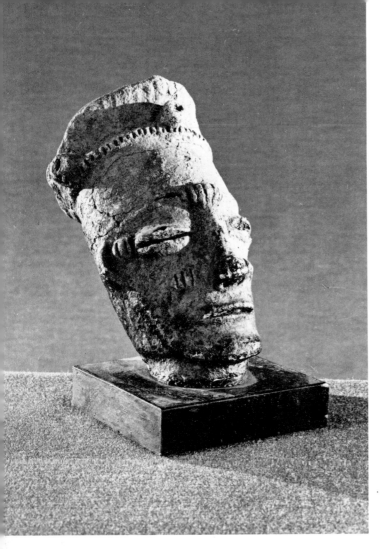

THE WESTERN SUDAN

177. Bracelet
SENUFO people, Ivory Coast
Brass, 2 5/8" (6.7 cm.) diameter
Acq. No. 7215

178. Balafon Musical Instrument
Upper Volta region
Wood and gourds
47 15/16" (121.8 cm.) long
Acq. No. 7453

179. Whistle
Upper Volta Region
Wood, 3 1/2" (8.9 cm.) long
Acq. No. 7456

180. Whistle
Upper Volta region
Wood, 3 7/8" (9.8 cm.) long
Acq. No. 7455

181. Powder Horn
Western Sudan region
Ivory, hide, and fiber
15 9/16" (39.5 cm.) long
Acq. No. 7280

185/183/186

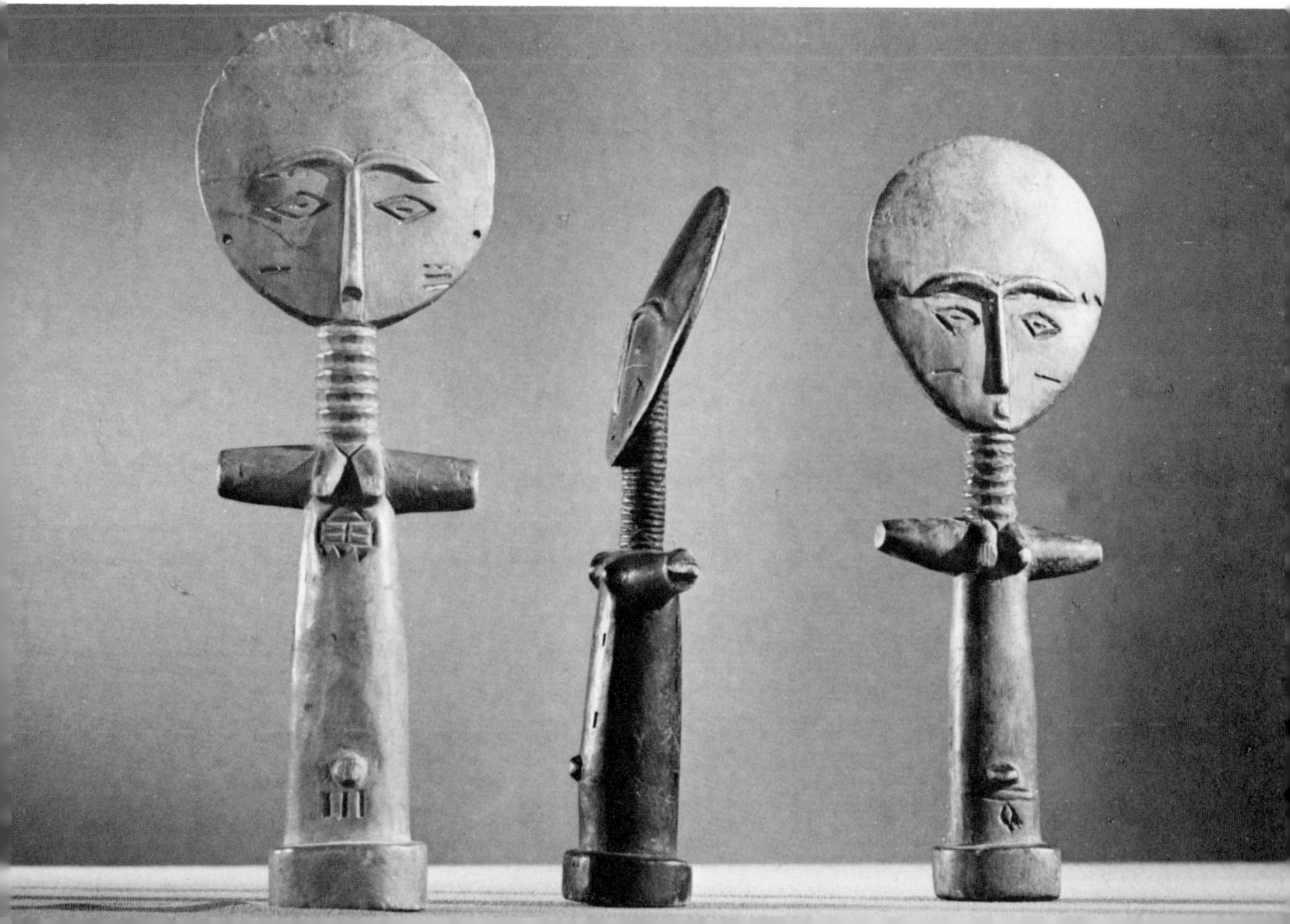

THE WESTERN GUINEA COAST

182. Reliquary Head
    AGNI people, Ivory Coast
    Terra Cotta, 6 3/8" (16.3 cm.) high
    Acq. No. 7194

183. Fertility Figure
    ASHANTI people, Ghana
    Wood, 9 3/8" (23.8 cm.) high
    Acq. No. 7156

184. Fertility Figure
    ASHANTI people, Ghana
    Wood, 11" (27.9 cm.) high
    Acq. No. 6981

185. Fertility Figure
    ASHANTI people, Ghana
    Wood, 11 1/4" (28.6 cm.) high
    Acq. No. 7257

186. Fertility Figure
    ASHANTI people, Ghana
    Wood, 10 5/8" (27 cm.) high
    Acq. No. 7155

187. Drum
    ASHANTI people, Ghana
    Wood, 36" (91.4 cm.) high
    Acq. No. 7461

188. Stool
    ASHANTI people, Ghana
    Wood, 19 1/8" (48.6 cm.) long
    Acq. No. 7355

189. Stool
    ASHANTI people, Ghana
    Wood, 17 1/2" (44.4 cm.) long
    Acq. No. 7356

190. Stool
    ASHANTI people, Ghana
    Wood, 16 3/4" (42.5 cm.) long
    Acq. No. 7353

188/191/192

191. Stool
ASHANTI people, Ghana
Wood, 27 1/4'' (69.2 cm.) long
Acq. No. 7357

192. Stool
ASHANTI people, Ghana
Wood, 17 7/16'' (44.3 cm.) long
Acq. No. 7354

193. Chair
ASHANTI people, Ghana
Wood with metal
28 1/8'' (71.4 cm.) high
Acq. No. 7338

194. Comb
ASHANTI people, Ghana
Wood, 11 1/8'' (28.2 cm.) long
Acq. No. 7276

195. Ceremonial Sword
ASHANTI people, Ghana
Metal and wood
27 1/8'' (68.9 cm.) long
Acq. No. 7478

196. Gold Weights (15)
ASHANTI people, Ghana
Brass, approx. 1/2'' to 1'' (1.3 to 2.6 cm.)
Acq. No. 7197

202

THE WESTERN SUDAN

197. Harvest Fertility Figure
BAGA people, Guinea
Wood, 37 3/16'' (94.4 cm.) long
Acq. No. 7304

198. Shoulder Mask
BAGA people, Guinea
Wood with metal
47 5/8'' (120.8 cm.) high
Acq. No. 7462

199. Harvest Fertility Figure
BAGA people, Guinea
Wood, 34 11/16'' (87.5 cm.) long
Acq. No. 7266

200. Mask
BASSA people, Liberia
Wood, 7 1/2'' (19 cm.) high
Acq. No. 7151

201. Standing Monkey Figure
BAULE people, Ivory Coast
Wood, 21 1/2'' (54.6 cm.) high
Acq. No. 7183

202. Drum
BAULE people, Ivory Coast
Wood with pigment,
25 1/2'' (64.8 cm.) high
Acq. No. 7437

203. Loom Heddle Pulley
BAULE people, Ivory Coast
Wood, 8 3/4'' (22.2 cm.) high
Acq. No. 7177

204. Chief's Stool
BAULE people, Ivory Coast
Wood with fiber, 31 3/4'' (80.5 cm.) high
Acq. No. 7078

205. Monkey Figure
BAULE people, Ivory Coast
Wood with encrustation
22 1/4'' (56.2 cm.) high
Acq. No. 7184

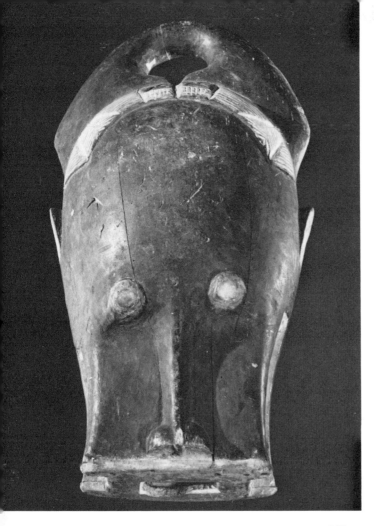

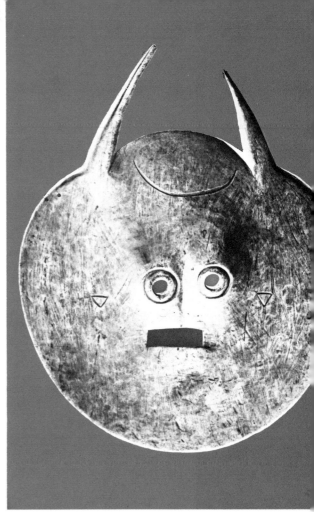

207

208

206. Standing Male Figure
     BAULE people, Ivory Coast
     Wood with pigment
     15 15/16'' (40.5 cm.) high
     Acq. No. 7147

207. Buffalo Mask
     BAULE people, Ivory Coast
     Wood with pigment
     20'' (50.8 cm.) high
     Acq. No. 7290

208. Cow Mask
     BAULE people, Ivory Coast
     Wood, 14 1/2'' (36.9 cm.) high
     Acq. No. 7092

209. Standing Figure
     BAULE people, Ivory Coast
     Wood with encrustation
     7 7/16'' (18.9 cm.) high
     Acq. No. 7154

210. Standing Female Figure
     BAULE people, Ivory Coast
     Wood, 18 3/4'' (47.7 cm.) high
     Acq. No. 7095

211. Divination Bowl
     BAULE people, Ivory Coast
     Wood, gourd, and hide
     7'' (17.8 cm.) high
     Acq. No. 7086

212. Standing Male Figure
     BAULE people, Ivory Coast
     Wood, 30 1/2'' (77.4 cm.) high
     Acq. No. 7193

213. Standing Female Figure
     BAULE people, Ivory Coast
     Wood, 17'' (43.2 cm.) high
     Acq. No. 7348

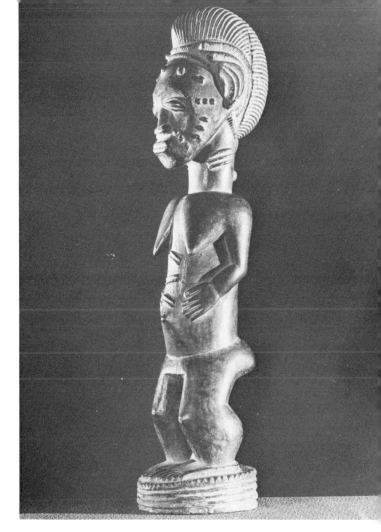

215

214. Standing Female Figure
     BAULE people, Ivory Coast
     Wood, 15'' (38.1 cm.) high
     Acq. No. 7166

215. Standing Female Figure
     BAULE people, Ivory Coast
     Wood, 15 1/4'' (38.7 cm.) high
     Acq. No. 7133

216. Horn
     BAULE people, Ivory Coast
     Ivory, 16 15/16'' (43 cm.) long
     Acq. No. 7187

217. Seated Female Figure
     BAULE people, Ivory Coast
     Wood, 16 5/8" (42.3 cm.) high
     Acq. No. 7130

218. Standing Female Figure
     BAULE people, Ivory Coast
     Wood, 11" (28 cm.) high
     Acq. No. 7134

219. Standing Female Figure
     BAULE people, Ivory Coast
     Wood, 17 9/16" (44.6 cm.) high
     Acq. No. 7142

220. Two Alligators
     BAULE people, Ivory Coast
     Wood with inlaid ivory
     26" (66 cm.) long
     Acq. No. 7104

221. Fly Whisk
     BAULE people, Ivory Coast
     Wood with hair, 15 1/8" (38.4 cm.) long
     Acq. No. 7349

222. Fly Whisk Head
     BAULE people, Ivory Coast
     Wood, 15 5/16" (38.9 cm.) long
     Acq. No. 7345

223. Fly Whisk Head
     BAULE people, Ivory Coast
     Wood, 16 1/4" (41.3 cm.) long
     Acq. No. 7344

224. Fly Whisk Head
     BAULE people, Ivory Coast
     Wood, 13 7/8" (35.2 cm.) long
     Acq. No. 7158

225. Fly Whisk Head
     BAULE people, Ivory Coast
     Wood, 15 7/8" (40.3 cm.) long
     Acq. No. 7157

221

226. Loom Heddle Pulley
     BAULE people, Ivory Coast
     Wood, 5 1/2'' (14 cm.) high
     Acq. No. 7170

227. Loom Heddle Pulley
     BAULE people, Ivory Coast
     Wood, 6 7/16'' (16.3 cm.) high
     Acq. No. 7173

228. Whip
     BAULE people, Ivory Coast
     Wood with cloth and hide
     34'' (86.3 cm.) long
     Acq. No. 7346

229. Spoon
     BAULE people, Ivory Coast
     Wood, 18 5/16'' (46.5 cm.) long
     Acq. No. 7254

230. Spoon
     BAULE people, Ivory Coast
     Wood, 19 5/8'' (49.9 cm.) long
     Acq. No. 7252

231. Loom Heddle Pulley
BAULE people, Ivory Coast
Wood, 11'' (28 cm.) high
Acq. No. 7176

232. Loom Heddle Pulley
BAULE people, Ivory Coast
Wood, 6 15/16'' (17.7 cm.) high
Acq. No. 7255

233. Stool
BAULE people, Ivory Coast
Wood, 16 3/4'' (42.5 cm.) long
Acq. No. 7090

234. Standing Male Figure
BAULE people, Ivory Coast
Wood, 15 9/16'' (39.5 cm.) high
Acq. No. 7146

231

234

THE WESTERN GUINEA COAST

235. Mask
     BAULE people, Ivory Coast
     Wood with pigment
     14 3/8'' (36.5 cm.) high
     Acq. No. 7186

236. Mask
     DAN-NGERE people, Ivory Coast
     Wood with fiber, 13'' (33 cm.) high
     Acq. No. 7230

237. Mask
     DAN-NGERE people, Ivory Coast
     Wood with cloth
     14 11/16'' (37.3 cm.) high
     Acq. No. 7109

238. Mask
     DAN-NGERE people, Ivory Coast
     Wood with cloth
     11 7/8'' (30.2 cm.) high
     Acq. No. 7195

239. Mask
     DAN-NGERE people, Ivory Coast
     Wood with metal
     10 1/4'' (26 cm.) high
     Acq. No. 7111

240. Mask
     DAN-NGERE people, Ivory Coast
     Wood with hair and feathers
     10 1/2'' (26.7 cm.) high
     Acq. No. 7120

238

239

241. Mask
DAN-NGERE people, Ivory Coast
Wood with cloth and hair
11 1/4'' (28.5 cm.) high
Acq. No. 7163

242. Mask
DAN-NGERE people, Ivory Coast
Wood with metal
8 15/16'' (22.8 cm.) high
Acq. No. 7112

243. Mask
DAN-NGERE people, Ivory Coast
Wood with shells
9 3/4'' (24.8 cm.) high
Acq. No. 7162

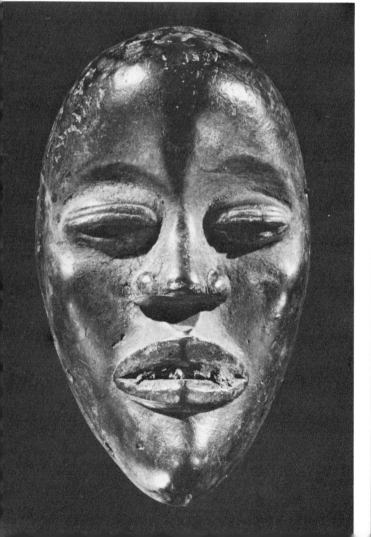

THE WESTERN GUINEA COAST

244. Mask
DAN-NGERE people, Ivory Coast
Wood with hair
10 1/2'' (26.7 cm.) high
Acq. No. 7159

245. Mask
DAN-NGERE people, Ivory Coast
Wood with fiber, 13'' (33 cm.) high
Acq. No. 7230

246. Mask
DAN-NGERE people, Ivory Coast
Wood, 11 1/2'' (29.3 cm.) high
Acq. No. 7113

247. Mask
DAN-NGERE people, Ivory Coast
Wood with metal and hair
10 1/8'' (25.7 cm.) high
Acq. No. 6956

248. Mask
DAN-NGERE people, Ivory Coast
Wood, 11'' (28 cm.) high
Acq. No. 7150

249. Standing Female Figure
DAN-NGERE people, Ivory Coast
Wood, 37 1/4'' (94.5 cm.) high
Acq. No. 7192

250. Spoon
DAN-NGERE people, Ivory Coast
Wood with metal
27'' (68.7 cm.) long
Acq. No. 7188

251. Mask
DAN-NGERE people, Ivory Coast
Wood with fur and metal
11 3/4'' (29.8 cm.) high
Acq. No. 7129

252. Bracelet
DAN-MANO people, Ivory Coast
Brass, 4 1/2'' (11.5 cm.) diameter
Acq. No. 7181

244

246

247

241

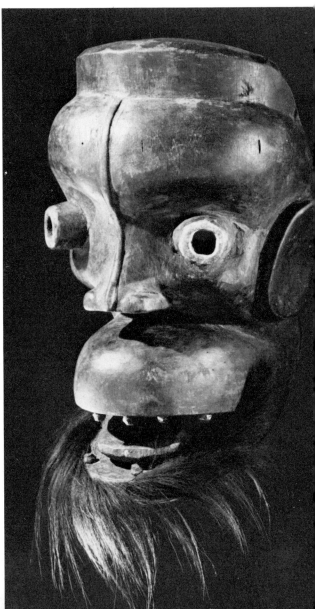

245

253. Bracelet
DAN-MANO people, Ivory Coast
Brass, 6 1/16" (15.5 cm.) diameter
Acq. No. 7179

254. Bracelet
DAN-MANO people, Ivory Coast
Brass, 5 1/8" (13 cm.) diameter
Acq. No. 7178

255. Bracelet
DAN-MANO people, Ivory Coast
Brass, 4 13/16" (12.2 cm.) diameter
Acq. No. 7180

256. Bracelet
DAN-MANO people, Ivory Coast
Brass, 5 1/2" (14 cm.) diameter
Acq. No. 7182

257. Rattle
DIONLA people, Ivory Coast
Wood and hide
23 5/8" (60 cm.) long
Acq. No. 7097

258. Musical Instrument
FULANI people, Liberia
Wood and hide
26 1/2" (67.4 cm.) long
Acq. No. 7247

259. Musical Instrument
FULANI people, Liberia
Wood and hide
27" (68.6 cm.) long
Acq. No. 7489

260. Turtle
GARBI people, Liberia
Wood with cloth and teeth
16 1/4" (41.2 cm.) long
Acq. No. 7234

261. Textile
Ghana region
Silk and cotton
4 1/4" x 78" (10.8 x 198.1 cm.)
Acq. No. 6920

262. Textile
Ghana region
Silk and cotton
3 3/4" x 73" (9.5 x 185.4 cm.)
Acq. No. 6921

263. Textile
Ghana region
Silk and cotton
4" x 72" (10.2 x 184.1 cm.
Acq. No. 6922

264. Textile
Ghana region
15 3/4" x 74" (40 x 187.9 cm.)
Acq. No. 6923

268

265. Bracelet
GIO people, Liberia
Brass, 6" (15.3 cm.) diameter
Acq. No. 7205

266. Helmet Mask
GOLA people, Liberia
Wood with fiber
23 1/4" (59 cm.) high
Acq. No. 7096

267. Helmet Mask
GOLA people, Liberia
Wood with fiber
27 3/4" (70.5 cm.) high
Acq. No. 7102

268. Helmet Mask
GOLA/DE/VAI people, Liberia
Wood, 14 3/4" (37.5 cm.) high
Acq. No. 7105

269. Helmet Mask
GOLA/DE/VAI people, Liberia
Wood, 16 1/4" (41.3 cm.) high
Acq. No. 7132

270. Helmet Mask
GOLA/DE/VAI people, Liberia
Wood, 13 1/8" (33.3 cm.) high
Acq. No. 7106

269

271. Mask
GREBO people, Liberia
Wood, 12'' (30.5 cm.) high
Acq. No. 7110

272. Mask
GREBO people, Liberia
Wood, 5 1/8'' (13.4 cm.) high
Acq. No. 7152

273. Drum
GREBO people, Liberia
Wood, 72 15/16'' (185.1 cm.) high
Acq. No. 7426

274. Bowl
GREBO people, Liberia
Wood, 11 3/8'' (29 cm.) diameter
Acq. No. 7082

275. Bowl
GREBO people, Liberia
Wood, 10 3/8'' (26.4 cm.) diameter
Acq. No. 7081

276. Bowl
BREBO people, Liberia
Wood, 10 3/8'' (26.4 cm.) diameter
Acq. No. 7080

271

280

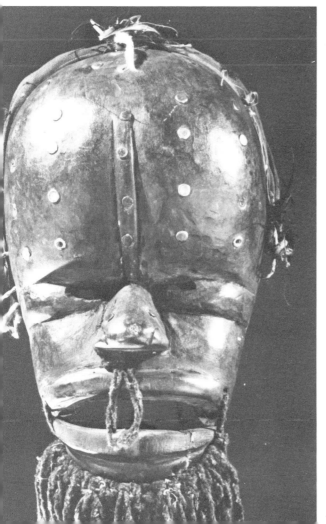

THE WESTERN GUINEA COAST

277. Standing Female Figure
     Guinea region
     Wood, 12 13/16" (32.6 cm.) high
     Acq. No. 7139

278. Mask
     GURO people (?), Ivory Coast
     Wood, 19" (48.2 cm.) high
     Acq. No. 7114

279. Mask
     GURO people (?), Ivory Coast
     Wood with pigment
     14 3/16" (36.1 cm.) high
     Acq. No. 7148

280. Mask
     GURO people, Ivory Coast
     Wood, 12 9/16" (31.9 cm.) high
     Acq. No. 7149

281. Loom Heddle Pulley
     Ivory Coast region
     Wood, 6 1/8" (15.7 cm.) high
     Acq. No. 7174

282. Loom Heddle Pulley
     Ivory Coast region
     Wood, 6 5/16" (16 cm.) high
     Acq. No. 7169

283. Loom Heddle Pulley
     Ivory Coast region
     Wood, 5 5/8" (14.3 cm.) high
     Acq. No. 7171

284. Loom Heddle Pulley
Ivory Coast region
Wood, 9 3/8" (23.8 cm.) high
Acq. No. 7172

285. Bracelet
Ivory Coast region
Bronze, 4 1/8" (10.5 cm.) diameter
Acq. No. 7447

286. Bracelet
Ivory Coast region
Ivory, 2 1/8" (5.4 cm.) diameter
Acq. No. 7201

287. Bracelet
Ivory Coast region
Bronze, 3 1/8" (8 cm.) diameter
Acq. No. 7448

288. Ring
Ivory Coast region
Bronze, 1 3/4" (4.5 cm.) diameter
Acq. No. 7449

289. Seven Amulets
Ivory Coast region
Brass, approx. 1"x1" (2.6 x 2.6 cm.)
Acq. No. 7196

316

344-350

356

290. Bracelet
Ivory Coast region
Ivory, 3 9/16" (9.1 cm.) diameter
Acq. No. 7198

291. Painted Fabric
Ivory Coast region
Cotton, 86" x 61" (218.3 x 154.9 cm.)
Acq. No. 7235

292. Warrior's Shirt
Ivory Coast region
Cotton with pigment
30" x 30" (76.2 x 76.2 cm.)
Acq. No. 7245

293. Necklace
Ivory Coast region
Bronze, 20" (50.8 cm.) long
Acq. No. 7454

294. Necklace
Ivory Coast region
Glass, multicolored
29" (73.8 cm.) long
Acq. No. 6939

295. Necklace
Ivory Coast region
Stone, 34" (86.3 cm.) long
Acq. No. 6938

296. Necklace
Ivory Coast region
Bronze, 26" (66 cm.) long
Acq. No. 7446

297. Necklace
Ivory Coast region
Glass, multicolored
30" (76.2 cm.) long
Acq. No. 6689

298. Bracelet
Ivory Coast region
Ivory, 2 1/16" (5.3 cm.) diameter
Acq. No. 7202

299. Bracelet
Ivory Coast region
Ivory, 3 5/16" (8.4 cm.) diameter
Acq. No. 7200

300. Mask
KISSI people (?), Guinea
Wood with horn and encrustation
28 1/2" (72.4 cm.) high
Acq. No. 7343

301. Mask
KRAN people, Ivory Coast
Wood with pigment and cloth
13 1/4" (33.7 cm.) high
Acq. No. 7115

302. Mask
KRAN people, Ivory Coast
Wood with cloth
8 3/4" (22.2 cm.) high
Acq. No. 7161

303. Bracelet
KRAN people, Ivory Coast
Brass, 4" (10.2 cm.) diameter
Acq. No. 7207

304. Bracelet
KRU people, Liberia
Bronze, 2 1/4" (5.7 cm.) diameter
Acq. No. 7243B

305. Bracelet
KRU people, Liberia
Bronze, 3" (7.6 cm.) diameter
Acq. No. 7243A

306. Ring
KRU people, Liberia
Brass, 1 7/8" (4.8 cm.) diameter
Acq. No. 7220

307. Warrior's Shirt with Amulets
Liberia region
Cotton, handwoven; leather amulets
26" x 21" (66 x 53.3 cm.)
Acq. No. 7236

381

THE WESTERN GUINEA COAST

308. Textile
     Liberia region
     Cotton, handwoven
     62" x 84" (157.4 x 213.3 cm.)
     Acq. No. 4612

309. Textile
     Liberia region
     Cotton, handwoven
     48" x 78" (121.8 x 198.2 cm.)
     Acq. No. 7248

310. Textile
     Liberia region
     Cotton, handwoven
     28" x 83" (71.1 x 210.7 cm.)
     Acq. No. 7249

311. Game Board
     Liberia region
     Wood, 26 15/16" (68.4 cm.) long
     Acq. No. 7101

312. Bracelet
     Liberia region
     Ivory, 3 11/16" (9.6 cm.) diameter
     Acq. No. 7206

313. Bracelet
     Liberia region
     Brass, 6 7/8" (17.5 cm.) diameter
     Acq. No. 7219

314. Bracelet
     Liberia region
     Brass, 3 1/4" (8.3 cm.) diameter
     Acq. No. 7221

315. Mask
     LOGI people, Senegal
     Wood, 28" (71.1 cm.) high
     Acq. No. 7282

316. Helmet Mask
     LOMA people, Liberia
     Wood, 12 7/8" (32.7 cm.) high
     Acq. No. 7107

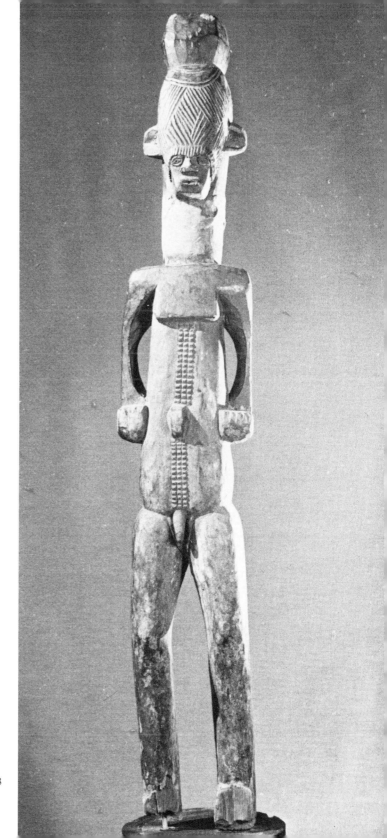

358

317. Standing Male Figure
MANDINGO people, Liberia/Guinea
Wood, 11" (27.9 cm.) high
Acq. No. 7135

318. Mask
MANO people, Liberia
Wood, 3 3/4" (9.5 cm.) high
Acq. No. 7153

319. Mask
MENDE people, Liberia
Wood with fiber
22 3/8" (56.9 cm.) high
Acq. No. 7079

320. Helmet Mask
MENDE people, Liberia
Wood with fiber
15 5/8" (39.3 cm.) high
Acq. No. 7123

321. Standing Female Figure
MENDE people, Liberia
Wood, 16 15/16" (43 cm.) high
Acq. No. 7136

369

322. Drum
     NGERE people, Ivory Coast
     Wood with pigment
     57 3/16" (145.3 cm.) long
     Acq. No. 7337

323. Textile
     Senegal region
     Cotton, dyed
     35" x 130" (177.8 x 330 cm.)
     Acq. No. 7492

324. Textile
     Senegal region
     Cotton, dyed
     31" x 108" (78.8 x 274.2 cm.)
     Acq. No. 7498

325. Textile
     Senegal region
     Cotton, tied before dyeing
     52" (132 cm.) long
     Acq. No. 7503

326. Textile
     Senegal region
     Cotton, tied before dyeing
     15" x 21" (38.1 x 53.3 cm.)
     Acq. No. 7504

327. Textile
     Senegal region
     Cotton, tied before dyeing
     15" x 32" (38.1 x 81.2 cm.)
     Acq. No. 7505

328. Textile
     Senegal region
     Cotton with wax resist
     35" x 112" (88.8 x 284.4 cm.)
     Acq. No. 7496

329. Textile
     Senegal region
     Cotton, dyed
     35" x 128" (88.8 x 325 cm.)
     Acq. No. 7497

371

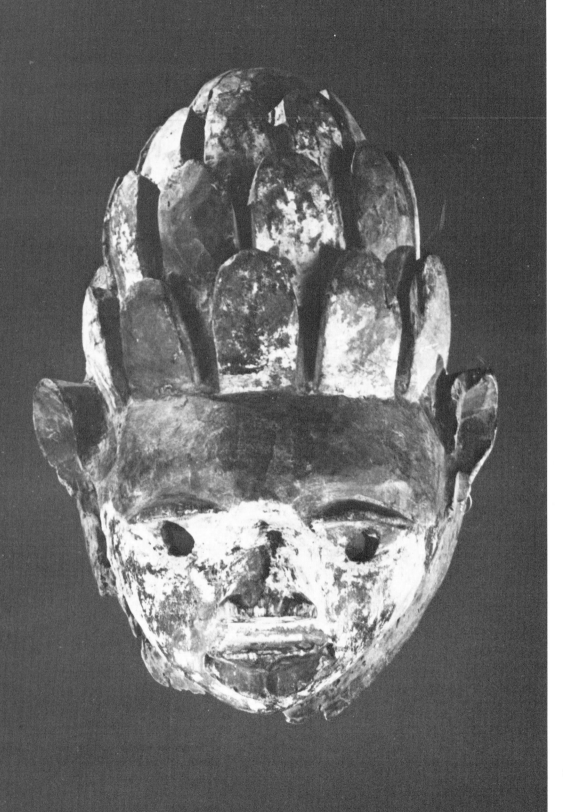

372

THE WESTERN GUINEA COAST

330. Textile
Senegal region
Cotton, dyed
31" x 112" (78.8 x 284.4 cm.)
Acq. No. 7499

331. Textile
Senegal region
Cotton, dyed
30" x 116" (76.1 x 294.5 cm.)
Acq. No. 7500

332. Textile
Senegal region
Cotton, dyed
31" x 144" (78.8 x 365.6 cm.)
Acq. No. 7501

333. Textile
Senegal region
Cotton, dyed
35" x 132" (88.8 x 335.2 cm.)
Acq. No. 7502

334. Textile
Senegal region
Cotton, dyed
31" x 108" (78.8 x 274.2 cm.)
Acq. No. 7495

335. Textile
Senegal region
Cotton with wax resist
36" x 37 1/2" (91.5 x 95.2 cm.)
Acq. No. 7490

336. Textile
Senegal region
Cotton with wax resist
35" x 132" (88.9 x 305.8 cm.)
Acq. No. 7493

337. Textile
Senegal region
Cotton, dyed
35" x 128" (88.9 x 325 cm.)
Acq. No. 7494

338. Textile
Senegal region
Cotton, dyed
31" x 114" (78.8 x 289.5 cm.)
Acq. No. 7491

339. Textile Printing Block
Senegal region
Wood, 4 3/4" x 4 3/4" (11.8 x 11.8 cm.)
Acq. No. 7506

340. Bracelet
Senegal region
Bronze, 11" (28 cm.) long
Acq. No. 7445

341. Bowl
Senegal region
Wood with pigment
13 1/8" (33.3 cm.) diameter
Acq. No. 7131

342. Bracelet
TOMA people, Guinea
Brass, 3 3/4" (9.6 cm.) diameter
Acq. No. 7217

343. Bracelet
TOMA people, Guinea
Brass, 3 7/8" (9.6 cm.) diameter
Acq. No. 7218

344. Brooch
WOLOF people, Senegal
Silver with gold wash
1 1/2" (3.8 cm.) diameter
Acq. No. 7443

345. Earrings
WOLOF people, Senegal
Silver with gold wash
1" (2.6 cm.) diameter
Acq. No. 7444

346. Necklace
WOLOF people, Senegal
Silver with gold wash
24" (61 cm.) long
Acq. No. 7442

347. Hair Ornament
WOLOF people, Senegal
Silver with gold wash
1 3/4" (4.5 cm.) diameter
Acq. No. 7440

348. Hair Ornament
WOLOF people, Senegal
Silver with gold wash
2" (5.1 cm.) diameter
Acq. No. 7439

349. Hair Ornament
WOLOF people, Senegal
Silver with gold wash
2 1/4" (5.8 cm.) diameter
Acq. No. 7438

350. Hair Ornament
WOLOF people, Senegal
Silver with gold wash
1 3/4" (4.5 cm.) diameter
Acq. No. 7441

351. Mask
Cameroon people
Wood with pigment
17 1/4" (43.8 cm.) high
Acq. No. 7226

352. Spoon
Cameroon people
Wood, 11 3/16" (28.4 cm.) long
Acq. No. 7250

353. Necklace
Cameroon people
Bronze with stone and glass beads
26" (66 cm.) long
Acq. No. 7317

354. Necklace
Cameroon people
Bronze, 30" (76.2 cm.) long
Acq. No. 7319

355. Necklace
Cameroon people
Bronze, 25" (63.5 cm.) long
Acq. No. 7318

356. Helmet Mask
EKOI people, Nigeria
Wood with hide
15 3/4" (40 cm.) high
Acq. No. 7083

357. Helmet Mask
EKOI people, Nigeria
Wood with hide
17 5/8" (44.8 cm.) high
Acq. No. 7077

358. Standing Male Figure
IBO people, Nigeria
Wood, 59" (150 cm.) high
Acq. No. 7119

359. Bracelet
IBO people, Nigeria
Ivory, 5 1/16" (12.9 cm.) diameter
Acq. No. 7203

360. Bracelet
IBO people, Nigeria
Ivory, 4" (10.2 cm.) diameter
Acq. No. 7199

361. Bracelet
IBO people, Nigeria
Ivory, 5 1/16" (12.9 cm.) diameter
Acq. No. 7204

362. Paddle
ITSEKRI people, Nigeria
Wood, 62 5/8" (159 cm.) long
Acq. No. 7428

363. Paddle
ITSEKRI people, Nigeria
Wood, 55 15/16" (141.9 cm.) long
Acq. No. 7427

364. Reliquary Figure
KOTA people, Gabon
Wood with copper
21 1/4" (54 cm.) high
Acq. No. 7458

365. Headrest for Two
Nigeria region
Wood, 21 7/8" (55.6 cm.) long
Acq. No. 7189

366. Textile
Nigeria region
Cotton, dyed
66" x 80" (167.6 x 203.1 cm.)
Acq. No. 6960

367. Body Mask
YORUBA people, Dahomey
Wood with pigment
21 3/4" (55.3 cm.) high
Acq. No. 7459

368. Drum
YORUBA people, Nigeria
Wood, hide, and metal
18 3/4" (47.6 cm.) high
Acq. No. 7240

369. Mask
YORUBA people, Nigeria
Wood, 11 3/4" (30 cm.) high
Acq. No. 7279

370. Mask
YORUBA people, Nigeria
Wood with pigment
7 15/16' (20 cm.) high
Acq. No. 7103

371. Twin Cult Figures
YORUBA people, Nigeria
Wood, 9 3/4" and 9 7/8"
(24.8 and 25.1 cm.) high
Acq. No. 7394

372. Mask
YORUBA people, Nigeria
Wood with pigment
11 15/16" (30.3 cm.) high
Acq. No. 7342

373. Equestrian Figure
YORUBA people, Nigeria
Wood with pigment
21" (53.3 cm.) high
Acq. No. 7341

374. Mask
YORUBA people, Nigeria
Wood with pigment
7 15/16" (20 cm.) high
Acq. No. 7103

378

376

NIGERIA, CAMEROON

384. Fly Whisk Head
YORUBA people, Nigeria
Wood, 12 1/4" (31.1 cm.) high
Acq. No. 7350

385. Divination Tray
YORUBA people, Nigeria
Wood, 15 1/2" (39.3 cm.) diameter
Acq. No. 7098

386. Divination Tray
YORUBA people, Nigeria
Wood
9 1/2" x 13 9/16" (24.1 x 34.4 cm.)
Acq. No. 7099

387. Standing Male Figure
BENA LULUA people, Central Congo
Wood, 38 3/8" (97.4 cm.) high
Acq. No. 7288

388. Mask
KUBA people, Central Congo
Wood with feathers
17" (43.2 cm.) high
Acq. No. 7269

389. Drinking Horn
KUBA people, Central Congo
Wood and metal, 11" (28 cm.) long
Acq. No. 7270

390. Finger Piano
KUBA people, Central Congo
Metal and wood
3 1/16" x 6 1/4" (7.7 x 15.9 cm.)
Acq. No. 7271

391. Cup
KUBA people, Central Congo
Wood, 5 1/16" (12.9 cm.) high
Acq. No. 6954

392. Box
KUBA people, Central Congo
Wood
6 3/4" x 4" x 2 3/4" (17.2 x 10.2 x 7 cm.)
Acq. No. 7272

396

393. Standing Male Figure
    NDENGESE people, Central Congo
    Wood, 38 1/2" (97.7 cm.) high
    Acq. No. 7287

394. Loom Heddle Pulley
    PENDE people, Southwestern Congo
    Wood, 8 1/16" (20.5 cm.) high
    Acq. No. 7175

395. Mask
    PENDE people, Southwestern Congo
    Wood with pigment
    9 1/4" (23.5 cm.) high
    Acq. No. 7268

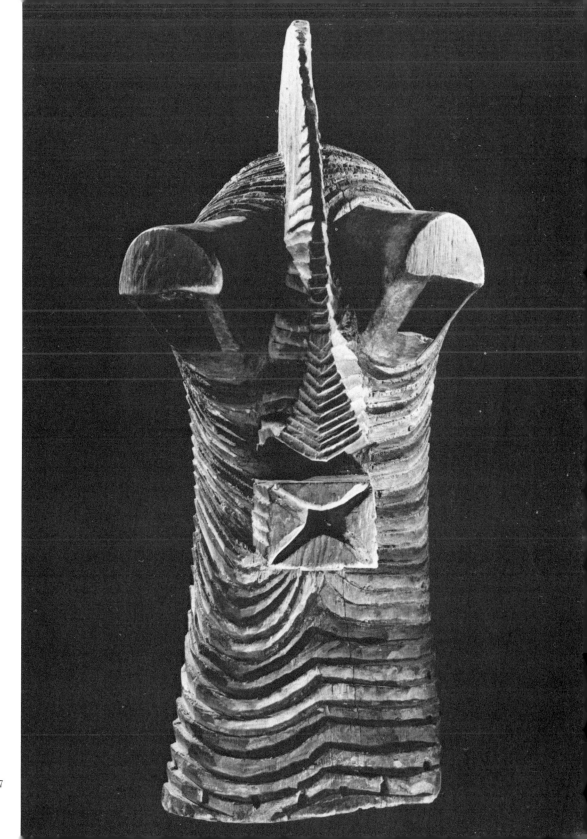

397

NIGERIA, CAMEROON

396. Fetish Figure
SALAMPASU people, Southern Congo
Wood with fiber
27" (68.6 cm.) high
Acq. No. 7285

397. Mask
SONGE people, Eastern Central Congo
Wood with pigment
24 1/4" (61.7 cm.) high
Acq. No. 7335

398. Fetish Figure
SUKU people, Southwestern Congo
Wood, 4 3/4" (12.1 cm.) high
Acq. No. 7275

399. Fetish Figure
TEKE people, Southwestern Congo
Wood with cloth
15" (38.1 cm.) high
Acq. No. 7168

400. Mask
TSAYE people, Southwestern Congo
Wood with pigment
14 1/4" (36.2 cm.) high
Acq. No. 7232

401. Mask
TSHOKWE people, Southern Congo
Wood with fiber
8 3/4" (22.2 cm.) high
Acq. No. 7267

402. Fetish Figure
YAKA people, Southwestern Congo
Wood and cloth
4 7/16" (11.3 cm.) high
Acq. No. 7274

403. Slit Drum
YAKA people, Southwestern Congo
Wood, 16 3/4" (42.5 cm.) high
Acq. No. 7273

404. Mask
West Africa region
Wood, 30 7/8'' (78.5 cm.) high
Acq. No. 7278

405. Mask with headpiece
West Africa region
Wood with pigment
50 1/2'' (128.3 cm.) high
Acq. No. 7277

406. Ceremonial Ax
West Africa region
Wood and metal
21'' (53.3 cm.) long
Acq. No. 7484

407. Carving Ax
West Africa region
Metal and wood
23 5/8'' (60 cm.) long
Acq. No. 7480

408. Carving Ax
West Africa region
Metal and wood
14 5/8'' (37.3 cm.) long
Acq. No. 7482

409. Carving Adz
West Africa region
Metal and wood
14 1/16'' (35.7 cm.) long
Acq. No. 7481

410. Toy Shotgun
West Africa region
Wood, 13 7/8'' (35.3 cm.) long
Acq. No. 7256

411. Shield
West Africa region
Wood with reed
30 15/16'' (78.5 cm.) high
Acq. No. 7468

412. Spear
West Africa region
Wood, metal, and hide
38 5/8'' (98 cm.) long
Acq. No. 7471

400

WEST AFRICA

413. Spear with Sheat
West Africa region
Wood, metal, and hide
54 9/16" (138.5 cm.) long
Acq. No. 7469

414. Spear Point
West Africa region
Metal, 12 7/8" (32.8 cm.) long
Acq. No. 7470

415. Spear
West Africa region
Metal and wood
52 5/16" (132.9 cm.) long
Acq. No. 7473

416. Fishing Spear
West Africa region
Metal and bamboo
64 1/4" (163.1 cm.) long
Acq. No. 7474

417. Spear Point
West Africa region
Metal, 19 5/8" (49.8 cm.) long
Acq. No. 7472

418. Spear Point
West Africa region
Metal, 27 5/8" (70.1 cm.) long
Acq. No. 7475

419. Spear Point
West Africa region
Metal, 20 1/4" (51.2 cm.) long
Acq. No. 7476

420. Spear Point
West Africa region
Metal, wood, and hide
17 1/8" (43.5 cm.) long
Acq. No. 7486

421. Spear Point
West Africa region
Metal and wood
20 7/8" (53 cm.) long
Acq. No. 7488

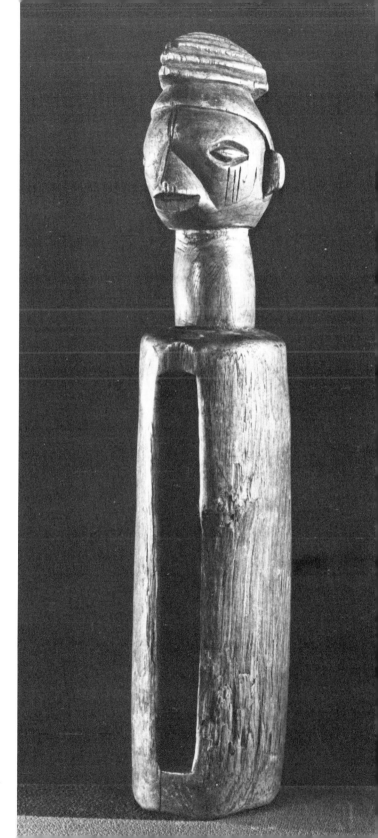

424. Bracelets (four)
West Africa region
Iron, 4 3/4'' (12 cm.) diameter
Acq. No. 7467

425. Bracelet
West Africa region
Metal, 3 7/8'' (9.9 cm.) diameter
Acq. No. 7261

426. Armlet
West Africa region
Brass, 3 3/16'' (8.1 cm.) diameter
Acq. No. 7262

427. Anklet
West Africa region
Metal, 4 1/2'' (11.5 cm.) diameter
Acq. No. 7260

428. Anklet
West Africa region
Brass, 3 3/4'' (9.5 cm.) diameter
Acq. No. 7258

429. Anklet
West Africa region
Brass, 4 1/2'' (11.5 cm.) diameter
Acq. No. 7259

422. Spear Point
West Africa region
Metal, wood, and reed
18 1/2'' (47 cm.) long
Acq. No. 7487

423. Musical Instrument
West Africa region
Wood, 19 3/4'' (50.2 cm.) long
Acq. No. 7479

265

303

WEST AFRICA

430. Textile
     West Africa region
     Cotton, hand printed and embroidered
     85" x 136" (215.8 x 345.3 cm.)
     Acq. No. 6919

431. Textile
     West Africa region
     Cotton, hand printed and embroidered
     84" x 136" (213.3 x 345.3 cm.)
     Acq. No. 6973

432. Bowl
     West Africa region
     Wood with pigment
     13 1/8" (33.3 cm.) diameter
     Acq. No. 7131

433. Necklace
     West Africa region
     Cast metal
     18 3/8" (46.7 cm.) high
     Acq. No. 7208

434. Mask
     West Africa region
     Wood with pigment
     14 3/16" (36.1 cm.) high
     Acq. No. 7148

433

434

**The University Museums
Illinois State University
Normal-Bloomington 61761**

Ewing Museum of Nations
Eyestone School Museum
Funk Gem and Mineral Museum
Hudelson Museum of Agriculture
Stevenson Memorial Room
University Historical Museum

Funds for producing this catalog
were provided jointly by
Illinois State University and the
Illinois State University Foundation.